NOTE: The small pictures that are printed to the upper right of some signs are suffixes. These include plurals, -ing and the possessive. Sign the suffix immediately after the root-word sign, as shown.

Use lots of facial expression, and always speak when signing.

The alphabet on the inside back cover will make many signs clearer. Hand-positions often represent the first letter of the word signed (e.g. "dad" — "D" and "big" — "B") For additional clarification, a glossary is printed at the back of the book which gives the description of how each sign is produced.

Modern Signs Press, Inc., solicits your comments and suggestions.

AT GRANDMA'S HOUSE

By Sue Johnson

Illustrated By Joni Herigstad

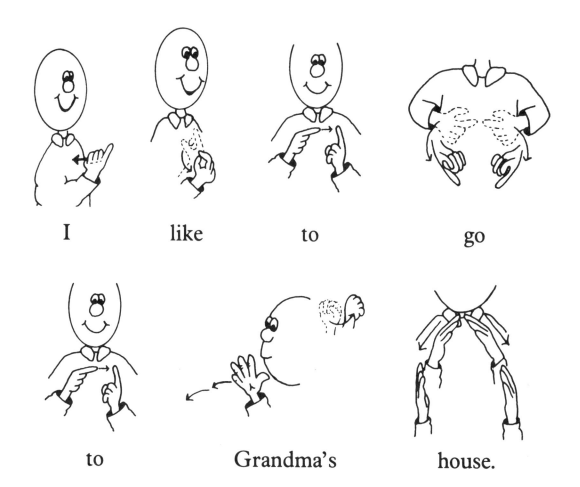

I   like   to   go

to   Grandma's   house.

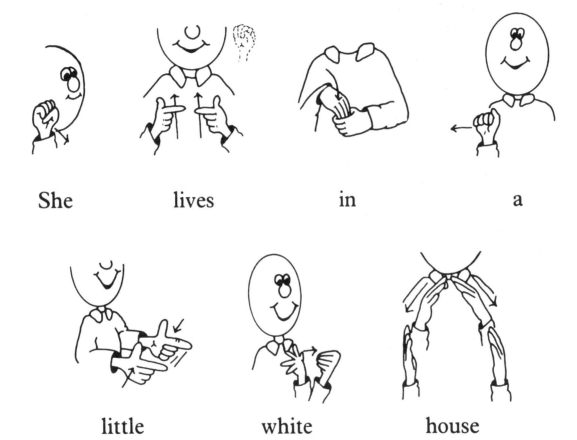

She   lives   in   a

little   white   house

with   a   green   roof.

My   Grandma   has

an   orange   kitten.

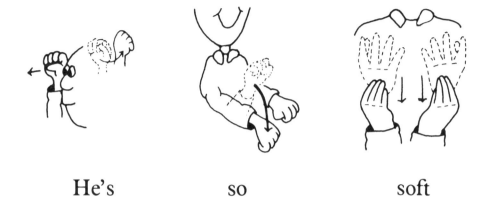

He's   so   soft

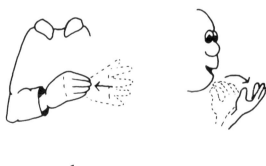

and   warm.

Grandma   and   I

make   cookies.

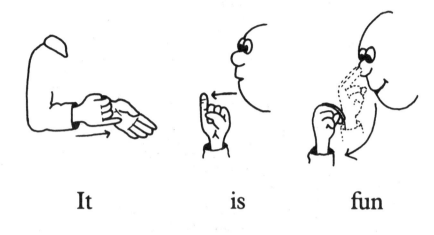

It   is   fun

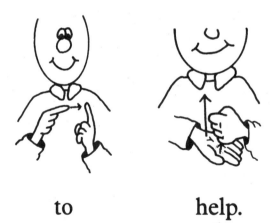

to   help.

Grandma   has   a

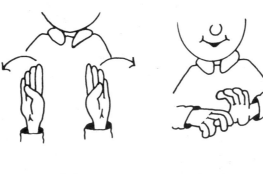

big   chair.

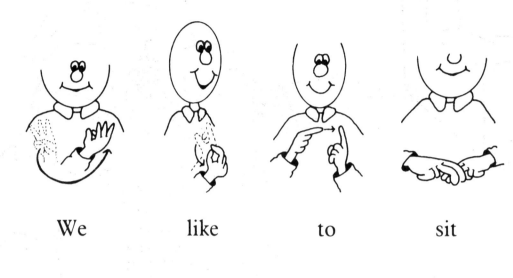

We   like   to   sit

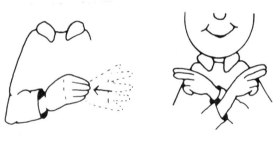

and   hug.

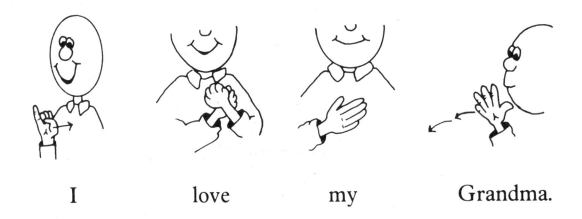

I   love   my   Grandma.

GLOSSARY

A–	Palm-out A moves slightly right
AN–	Palm-up A twists to palm-down
AND–	Palm-in, 5-hand, pulls to right, closing to a flat-O
BIG–	Palm-out B's arc sideways
CHAIR–	2 fingers "sit" on thumb of left C
COOKIE(s)–	Fingertips touch palm, twist and touch again, add S-hand
FUN–	Palm-in U on nose strokes downward to palm-in N
GO–	G-hands face each other, roll out to point forward
GRANDMA('s)–	From chin, palm-left 5 makes two arcs diagonally to right, add palm-out S twists inward
GREEN–	Palm-left G shakes
HAS=(HAVE+S)–	Fingertips of slightly bent hands approach and touch chest, add S-hand
HE('s)–	E at temple moves forward, slightly right, add palm-out S twists inward
HELP–	Palm lifts bottom of left S
HOUSE–	Flat palms outline roof and sides
HUG–	Hug self with H's
I–	Palm-left I-hand touches chest
IN–	Fingertips of right flat-O enter left O
IS–	I on chin moves straight forward
IT–	Tip of I touches palm of left hand
KITTEN–	Both K-hands moves to side from mouth; repeat

LIKE–	Palm-in L on chest moves forward, closing thumb and finger
LITTLE–	L-hands face each other, jerk slightly toward each other; repeat
LIVE(s)–	Palm-in L-Hands move up body; add S-hand
LOVE–	S-hands cross on heart
MAKE–	Side of S touches on side of S; both twist to palm-in and touch again
MY–	Flat hand palm on chest
ORANGE–	S squeezes in front of chin; repeat
ROOF–	R's outline a roof shape
SHE–	Palm-out E slides along jawline and forward
SIT–	Right U sits 2 fingers on left palm-down U
SO–	Right S moves sharply down, striking side of left S in passing
SOFT–	Palm-up open hands drop slightly, closing to flat-O's; repeat
TO–	Horizontal index finger approaches and touches left vertical index finger
WARM–	Flat-O at mouth opens slowly to 5-hand while moving slightly up and outward
WE–	W on right side of chest circles to left side
WHITE–	5 on chest moves outward, closing to a flat O
WITH—	A-hands together, palm to palm

*Glossary used by permission of Modern Signs Press, Inc.